What's Your FRASIER I.Q.?

What's Your FRASIER I.Q.?

501 Questions and Answers for Fans

ROBERT W. BLY

AURUM PRESS

First published in Great Britain 1997
by Aurum Press ltd, 25 Bedford Avenue, London WC1B 3AT
Copyright © 1996 by Robert W. Bly

A Citadel Press Book. Published by arrangement with Carol Publishing Group Inc.,
120 Enterprise Avenue, Secaucus, New Jersey 07094, USA

A catalogue record for this book is available from the British Library.

ISBN 1 85410 504 3

2 4 6 8 10 9 7 5 3 1

1998   2000   2001   1999   1997

Printed and bound in Great Britain by
Hartnolls Ltd, Bodmin

To Dave Bly—the world's best father—
in loving memory

ACKNOWLEDGMENTS

Thanks to my agent, Bonita Nelson, and my editors, Bruce Bender and Lynda Dickey, for their help and patience in getting this work completed.

Thanks also to Citadel Press and Mark Wenger for granting permission to include several great trivia questions from *The Cheers Trivia Book* in *What's Your Frasier I.Q.?*

CONTENTS

A Note on the Text

As you might imagine, many of these questions come from various episodes of *Frasier* and *Cheers*. Places and character names not shown on the screeen or listed in the credits are spelled phonetically—which means I guessed. So, please don't get too upset if you spot an occasional error.

INTRODUCTION

Television is best when it has something on its mind.
—NORMAN LEAR

Funny is an attitude.
—FLIP WILSON

Television will never improve unless the viewers speak up.
—DR. FRASIER CRANE

Frasier Crane was born in *Cheers*. Now his character lives on in his own series.

Usually sequels and spin-offs lack the quality of the original. Not true here. *Frasier* is, in many ways, as good as *Cheers*. In some ways, it's even better. The main character, Dr. Frasier Crane, has grown and added depth and maturity. He has a new career, a new family, and a new life. Yet friends from *Cheers* are never far, and many stop by Seattle for a visit now and then.

In the new series, Dr. Frasier Crane has been given a second life, and as a dedicated fan, I'm grateful. I love watching him in action—and interacting with Martin, Daphne, Roz, Bulldog, Niles, and the rest of the crew. Obviously you do too—or you wouldn't have bought this book.

Enjoy!

THE WHAT'S YOUR FRASIER I.Q.? SCORING SYSTEM

I wanted to put in a scoring system, but out of loyalty to Frasier, I couldn't. After all, he's a psychiatrist, and mental health professionals tend to frown on turning fun into a competitive activity. Frasier Crane wouldn't want you to go through these questions to see how you score or whether you beat someone else. He'd just want you to enjoy the experience. So do I. It's like miniature golf. Keep count if you want to. But don't get too hung up on the scoring. If you want to cheat and play a few holes over, be my guest.

What's Your
FRASIER
I.Q.?

LEVEL 1
TOSSED SALAD

1 When dining out, Frasier comments to Niles, "I've always dreamed of owning a four-star restaurant." What is Niles's reply?

2 Bebe Neuwirth, who plays Frasier's ex-wife Lilith, is a member of what high school graduating class?

3 In what hand does Martin Crane hold his cane when he walks?

4 When Niles buys Martin a do-it-yourself model boat kit, what kind of boat does he get him?

5 What brand of suit does Frasier wear?

6 What brand of pen does Frasier write with?

7 Employees at Frasier's radio station normally get what percentage annual raise?

8 Who is the executive producer of *Frasier*? (HINT: He has the same name as the actor who played Jim on *Taxi*.)

9 What illness does Niles's stable boy suffer?

10 Whom does Frasier refer to as the "princess of darkness," "a conniving femme fatale," and the "she-devil"?

11 Which employee at the radio station can faint at will?

12 What kind of car does Bulldog drive?

13 Who said, "How can we possibly use sex to get what we want? Sex *is* what we want"?

14 Match the Frasier character at left with the actor playing the character at right.

  1. Frasier Crane   A. David Hyde Pierce
  2. Niles Crane   B. Peri Gilpin
  3. Martin Crane   C. Kelsey Grammer
  4. Roz   D. Jane Leeves
  5. Daphne   E. John Mahoney
  6. Eddie   F. Moose
  7. Bulldog   G. Eric Lutes
  8. Tom Durant   H. Dan Butler

15 Which of Niles's patients is the sole survivor of a plane crash?

16 What name do Niles and Frasier give their business when they go into practice together?

17 How many people tune into Frasier's radio program each day?

18 On what floor of the building are the offices of Frasier's radio station located?

19 What organization names Maris Crane as its president?

20 What does Frasier say at the beginning of each show?

21 After leaving Boston, what city does Frasier move to?

22 What does Niles buy Maris for her fortieth birthday?

23 What does Daphne's brother Billy do for a living?

24 What is Niles's favorite vegetable dish? Martin's?

25 The author of the romance novel *Surrender to Bliss* lives in Frasier's building and has a crush on Martin. What is her name?

26 Who does Roz refer to as a "cold, repressed workaholic who has no life whatsoever"?

27 What type of piano does Frasier own? What did it cost?

28 What show airs on Frasier's radio station between eight and ten P.M. nightly?

29 Who is "dirty girl"?

30 What kind of car does Frasier drive?

31 What is Martin Crane's secret hobby that he keeps in a shoe box in his room?

32 Name the call letters of Frasier's radio station. Where is it on the AM dial?

33 Frasier gave the eulogy, which included a song, at whose funeral?

34 Where did Niles break his collarbone as a child—and how?

35 What type of gun does Martin Crane own?

36 Who hosted the religious show on Frasier's radio station until he was fired?

37 What subject did Frasier minor in at Harvard?

38 What member of the *Frasier* cast has been struck by lightning in real life?

39 What is the real name of the bar where Frasier hung out during his *Cheers* days? (HINT: *Cheers* was filmed in a real bar, and its name isn't Cheers.)

40 When was the pilot episode of *Frasier* filmed?

41 Aside from Kelsey Grammer, what other cast member of *Frasier* appeared in *Cheers*?

42 What nickname does Harlo Safford give to Niles?

43 Who pinned Niles to the ground with her trombone because he criticized her for not cleaning her spit valve?

44 Who tells Niles to "butter his buns"?

45 How many times has *Frasier* won the Emmy for Best TV Comedy?
    A. once
    B. twice
    C. three times
    D. four times
    E. never

46 When will *Frasier* go into syndication?
    A. 1996
    B. 1997
    C. 1998
    D. 1999
    E. never

47 Who is Frasier's business agent?

48 The actor who plays Bulldog did a guest appearance playing a gay art gallery owner on which NBC sitcom?

49 What well-known character actor played the psychiatrist who treated Niles and Frasier? (HINT: He also played the judge in *The Verdict*, a film starring Paul Newman as a down-on-his-luck attorney trying to win a medical malpractice case.)

50 Who decorated Lilith and Frasier's Boston apartment?

LEVEL 2
SCRAMBLED EGGS

1 Where did Lilith go after she left Frasier and moved out of their apartment?

2 Who was Frasier's first wife? (HINT: It's not Lilith.)

3 On what TV program do Niles and Frasier appear as expert witnesses for opposing counsel in a competency hearing?

4 Which of Frasier's female callers does Roz give advice to off the air?

5 What nickname did Niles want to be called by the string section of his high school orchestra?

6 Which of Daphne's relatives is blind, in her nineties, and has lost her sense of balance?

7 What instrument does Daphne play in one of the on-air promotion spots for *Frasier*?
   A. violin
   B. viola
   C. cello

D. bass

E. electric guitar

F. trumpet

8 When Frasier's agent gives the station manager a midnight deadline to reopen contract negotiations, at what time do they call him with their decision?

9 What type of ring did Vinny, a caller to Frasier's program, lose and ask Frasier to help him recover?

10 Who is Rosalinda?

11 What body of water is on Niles and Maris's estate?

12 What member of the Crane household is psychic?

13 What does Maris do to celebrate her thirty-fifth birthday?

14 Who created the character of Dr. Frasier Crane?

15 What happens to Niles when he gets angry?

16 Why does Maris get angry with her interior decorator?

17 Who hosts the radio show "Pet Chat"?

18 Who are Sky, Zena, and Slate?

19 How does Bebe Glasier describe Frasier's grip when he hugs her?

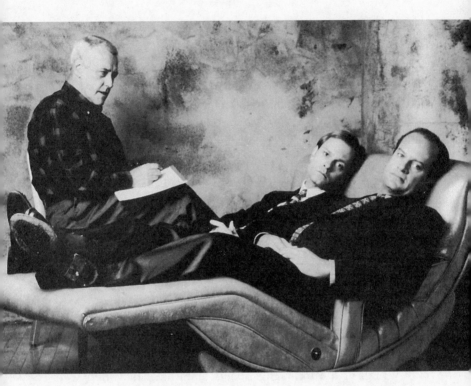

20 Who runs against Maris Crane for presidency of their wine club?

21 What drink does Niles usually order at the coffee bar?

22 When Niles wants to learn how to handle infants to decide whether he and Maris should have a child, what does he practice on?

23 Kelsey Grammer won an Emmy for his guest appearance on which TV comedy?

24 What did Kelsey Grammer do for a living in Rhode Island before he became a successful TV actor?

25 What happens to Niles whenever he lies?

26 Which *Frasier* star hosted the Twelfth Annual Soap Opera Awards show on NBC?
   A. Kelsey Grammer
   B. Jane Leeves
   C. Peri Gilpin
   D. David Hyde Pierce

27 What newspaper was published by Kelsey Grammer's father?

28 Which of the following *Cheers* stars have had their own TV shows or have done pilots?
   A. Kelsey Grammer
   B. George Wendt
   C. Rhea Perlman
   D. John Ratzenberger
   E. Jay Thomas
   F. Shelley Long
   G. Ted Danson

29 What actor plays Frasier's son when Frederick comes to visit his father at Christmas?

30 What is Niles's psychiatric specialty?

31 Who designed Frasier's Seattle apartment?

32 Where is *Frasier* filmed?

33 How much money does Frasier Crane earn annually?

34 What is the name of the coffee shop where Frasier and Niles hang out?

35 How much alimony does Lilith get from Frasier?

36 Bill and Hillary Clinton were in the audience of which prime-time television special starring the cast of *Frasier*?

37 Which of the following has *not* been used to describe Frasier's boss, Kate Costas?
  A. psycho perfectionist
  B. Gestapo agent
  C. little thug
  D. muscle woman

38 What does Bulldog mean when he describes a woman as "baggable"?

39 Why is Niles's credit card rejected when he attempts to treat Frasier to coffee at the coffee house?

40 What stripper was hired to entertain at Frasier's office Christmas party at the station?

41 What does Roz say is "over Bulldog's head"?

42 Frasier's son Frederick achieves maximum test scores in just two areas of child development. What are they?

43 Why doesn't Niles want to be sprayed with perfume in a department store?

44 Who is Olaf?

45 When Frasier was growing up, he spent a lot of time with which of his Jewish neighbors?

46 Which Crane lives in Kennibunkport, Maine?

47 What is Martin's favorite Christmas decoration?

48 How did Frasier pass the time at the first baseball game his father took him to when he was a child?

49 How does Niles explain the absence of Aunt Maris at Christmas to nephew Frederick?

50 What toy does Martin buy Frasier to give Frederick at Christmas?

LEVEL 3
A BIT CONFUSED

1 Who is the elderly absentminded waiter in one of Frasier and Niles's favorite restaurants?

2 Bebe Neuwirth (who plays Lilith on *Cheers*) plays an evil sorceress in the children's animated series *Aladdin*. What is the sorceress's name?

3 At what age did Frasier Crane allegedly lose his virginity?

4 Why did Kelsey Grammer walk off the set of *Frasier* after Moose switched dog food brands?

5 Which character did Kelsey Grammer guest-star as on *Star Trek: The Next Generation*?

6 Mercedes Ruehl, who plays Kate Costas on *Frasier*, appeared in which of the following feature films?
  A. *The Fisher King*
  B. *Lost in Yonkers*
  C. *Married to the Mob*
  D. *My Cousin Vinnie*
  E. *Police Academy IV*
  F. *Casino*

7 Which of the following Emmy awards have been won by
Frasier and its cast and crew?

   A. Lead Actress, Comedy Series
   B. Best Comedy Series
   C. Lead Actor, Comedy Series
   D. Best Supporting Actress, Comedy Series
   E. Best Directing, Comedy Series
   F. Best Supporting Actor, Comedy Series
   G. Best Writing, Comedy Series

8 Moose (the dog who plays Eddie) also appeared as Jim Carrey's dog in which movie?

9 In what device does Maris Crane float to relieve stress and tension?

10 What therapist treated Niles and Frasier together? In what country did he do his graduate work?

11 Which of the following ventures have Niles and Frasier tried doing together?
  A. starting their own cable TV show
  B. becoming partners in a psychiatric practice
  C. coauthoring a self-help book
  D. opening a restaurant
  E. giving karate lessons

12 After they successfully negotiate his contract and a big pay raise, what do Frasier and his business agent do to celebrate?

13 What foods does Kelsey Grammer sing about in the show's theme song?

14 In what colors does Daphne redecorate her room after Frasier offers to redo it in apology for entering without permission?

15 What is Frasier favorite collectible?

16 Name Frasier and Niles's favorite four-star restaurant.

17 Why is Frasier suspended from the air for a week?

18 Who is the author of the novel *The Rose and the Rapier*?

19 What is Martin Crane's favorite dessert?

20 Where is Roz from?

21 Which of the following is Martin Crane's preferred brand of beer?
   A. Budweiser
   B. Ballantine
   C. Schlitz
   D. Pabst Blue Ribbon
   E. Coors
   F. Molson

22 What is a McSession?

23 What character on *Frasier* has a tattoo?
   A. Martin Crane
   B. Bulldog
   C. Daphne
   D. Roz
   E. Duke

24 What type of gun does Niles buy for self-protection?

25 Frasier wants which piece of classical music as the new theme song for his radio show?

26 What awards has Kate Costas won in the radio business?

27 What type of noisy dog is in the apartment above Frasier's?

28 In what New York City bar did Kelsey Grammer wait tables?

29 Which *Frasier* cast member costarred with William Katt in the TV pilot *Lame Duck*?

30 Who plays Frasier's business agent?

31 When Maris leaves Niles, what type of therapy does Frasier recommend for his brother?
   A. primal scream
   B. Jungian analysis
   C. Freudian analysis
   D. smashing some of the expensive pieces of art Maris collects
   E. driving the Mercedes he gave Maris into the lake

32 Who is the author of the self-help book *Good Girls, Bad Boys*?

33 Which ex-professional athlete did Frasier once hire as a personal trainer, nutritionist, and athletic coach in an effort to tone up and lose weight?

34 What exercise class does Niles sign up for after the breakup of his marriage?

35 What does Ma Nature do?

36 What does Daphne serve Bebe with tea?

37 What does Frasier say he'd rather do than negotiate his contract?

38 Of whom does Niles say to Frasier, "She's the devil. Run fast, run far"?

39 How much of a raise does Frasier's annual contract call for him to receive before he renegotiates it?

40 Of whom does Frasier say to Niles, "She needs a man who can do more for her than smell her hair"?

41 What problem does Frasier have with the fireplace in his apartment?

42 Which of these books will you find on the shelves at Cafe Nervosa, Frasier's favorite coffee bar?
  A. *The Naked and the Dead*
  B. *Practical Aspects of Psychoanalysis*
  C. *Love Story*
  D. *The Science and Practice of Urban Land Valuation*
  E. *Baby and Child Care*
  F. *For Your Eyes Only*

43 What are the letters and numbers on Frasier's license plate?

44 What was the name of the song that was written by Martin Crane for Frank Sinatra but sung by a church choir at Aunt Louise's funeral?

45 If Martin can keep Eddie off Frasier's couch, Frasier says he won't do what to Eddie?

46 What is the name of the character Jane Leeves plays in *Miracle on 34th Street*?

47 What does Frasier usually wish his listeners at the close of his radio broadcast?

48 In Seattle, Frasier, Niles, the mayor, the commissioner of public safety, and the chief of surgery at St. Luke's hospital all belong to which group?

49 Daphne has a crush on a handsome contractor who is Niles's handyman. What is his name?

50 What type of coffee does Daphne serve in the Crane household?

- A. Colombian
- B. Brazilian
- C. English
- D. Costa Rican
- E. Chock Full o' Nuts

LEVEL 4
THE BLUES A-CALLIN'

1 What sweaty, cigar-puffing, overweight contractor is known as the "best ceiling man in Seattle"?

2 What does Niles say he never does?

3 What liberal Seattle politician visits the Crane household, much to Martin's annoyance?

4 Frasier says his show covers mental illnesses ranging from anorexia to what?

5 How many times per hour does Frasier read sponsors' ads on his show?

6 Niles observes that Daphne grates carrots at what precise angle?

7 Who is Murray Dingman?

8 Martin Crane admits he used to fantasize about Frasier's mother wearing which of the following?
  A. a bathing suit
  B. a miniskirt

C. a cheerleader's outfit

D. a nun's habit

E. a man's suit

9 What does the country western radio station in Chicago hire Kate to do?

10 Who says, "You can't let fear of rejection stop you"?

11 Which of the Cranes carries a cell phone?

12 Who does Kate date—casually—aside from Frasier?

13 Who arouses Niles when she falls asleep on his shoulder while they're watching TV together?

14 What does Frasier's blind date Donna do for a living?

15 What is Frasier's favorite color?

16 What is the name of Kate Costas's cat?

17 TRUE OR FALSE: Frasier wants to have more children.

18 How many Golden Globe awards was *Frasier* nominated for in 1995–96?

19 Who says, "I'm not one of those people for whom 'antique' is a verb"?

20 In what animated film does Bebe Neuwirth provide the voice of a sexy female dog?

21 What type of animal does Eddie catch in the park and leave half-eaten in the elevator?

22 Why do jockeys remind Niles of Maris?

23 What group does Frasier describe as "insufferable bores"?

24 What household accident did Niles and Frasier cause with a Bunsen burner when they were children?

25 Who says, "I believe in the strangeness of strangers"?

26 Who does Martin say was never good at making friends?

27 What is the "spuddy buddy"?

28 Where is Roz's former boyfriend Garth from? What does he keep in a trunk in his house?

29 What does Gerard want to do with Frasier?

30 What type of books does Frasier collect?

31 Who is "Dr. Revlon"?

32 What does Bob Reynolds say is the secret to good barbecue? What is his barbecue specialty dish?

33 What does Bob Reynolds do for a living?

34 What kind of breakfast drink does Daphne prepare for Martin?

35 What does Roz say when she wants to dump a boyfriend?

36 How does Niles compare psychiatry to pool cleaning?

37 When Kelsey Grammer says, "He played a good violin, badly," to whom is he referring?

38 Who calls Frasier "Mr. Quick Fix"?

39 How much does Niles charge for therapy?

40 What model of Mercedes does Niles drive?

41 How do you give someone a swirly?

42 Name the bully who picked on Niles during high school.

43 According to *Time* magazine, which Frasier star has been arrested for drunk driving?

44 Of whom is Niles speaking when he says, "She's my life!"?

45 How old is Maris's Guatemalan housekeeper? Who plays her?

46 What is the name of Kelsey Grammer's pet greyhound?

47 What type of psychiatrist is Frasier—Freudian or Jungian? What type is Niles?

48 On *Cheers*, Frasier said his father was in what profession (HINT: It was not a police officer.)

49 On what Norman Lear 1990s sitcom did David Hyde Pierce play a depressed congressman?

50 What *Frasier* star has a Jacuzzi, a pool, and a stone lion head fountain in his or her backyard?

LEVEL 5
THE ID AND THE EGO

1 What is the name of the chef Frasier and Niles hire to work in the kitchen of their failed restaurant venture? Who was his previous employer?

2 Frasier Crane's father owns a collector's baseball autographed by which major league player?

3 When Frasier dumped his first love, what did he leave on her pillow?

4 David Hyde Pierce plays a publishing executive in which Jack Nicholson film?

5 In what motion picture does John Mahoney romance Olivia Dukakis?

6 What was Frasier's favorite bar in Boston?

7 What was Martin Crane's favorite bar in Seattle?

8 What excuse did Niles and Frasier give to avoid a fight with the school bully?

9 Where did Frasier Crane earn his medical degree?

10 How many hours a day does Frasier work at his radio job?

11 In what country did Maris Crane's fencing instructor, Gunar, win the national fencing championship three times?

12 What does Niles call Gunar when he suspects Gunar has been sleeping with Maris?

13 Who is the principal director of *Frasier*?

14 What award did *Frasier* win from the Television Critics Association?

15 What does Roz tells Niles when she offers to give him a hickey?

16 How many brothers does Daphne have?

17 Why doesn't Niles buy Maris flowers?

18 Which *Frasier* cast member played opposite Christopher Plummer and James Earl Jones in *Othello*?

19 Who was the judge in the sanity hearing in which Niles appeared on TV as an expert witness?

20 What does Niles say he admires most about Frasier?

21 When Frasier performs as a clown at a children's birthday party, what happens when he pulls the handkerchief on his costume?

22 How old is Harlo Safford when his son takes legal action to have him declared mentally incompetent?

23 What "home remedy" does Martin use to treat a corn on his big toe?

24 What does Maris bathe in as a beauty treatment?

25 What song does Frasier usually sing at the annual public TV fund-raiser in Seattle?

26 What explanation does Niles give Frasier as to why he is carrying seven hundred dollars in his wallet?

27 Kelsey Grammer was featured in the TV miniseries *Washington* along with which former *Charlie's Angels* star?

28 Whose favorite expression was, "Stop crying, or I'll give you something to cry about"?

29 How does Martin propose to fix the scratch his chair made on Frasier's wood floor?

30 What item on Niles's to-do list has he not yet done?

31 What causes a fire in Frasier's apartment?

32 In an on-air promo for *Frasier*, Kelsey Grammer plays the NBC call letters on what musical instrument?

33 What allergy does Frasier have?

34 Who dreams of raising horses on a ranch in Montana?

35 What is Frasier's favorite city?

36 Which of these films does Niles rent for Martin to watch?
   A. *The French Connection*
   B. *Police Academy III*
   C. *Casablanca*
   D. *The Terminator*
   E. *Victor/Victoria*

37 Who said, "You never know if you're leaving a place too soon"?

38 Why does Daphne put a toothpick in the chicken breasts she is cooking?

39 How many kids does Kate Costas want to have with Frasier?

40 What does Martin add to his breakfast health drink to spice it up?

41 What character does Griffin Dunne play on an episode of *Frasier*?

42 When Roz tells Frasier, "They sort of frown on that in call-in shows," to what is she referring?

43 What is "nature's barbecue"?

44 Who cleans Niles's pool?

45 What is Bob Reynolds's favorite accessory?

46 Where does Kelsey Grammer live?

47 What type of car does Danny Creasel drive?

48 When Daphne tells Frasier, "There are some heads you shouldn't tamper with," to what is she referring?

49 What did Niles's high school classmates chant when a bully stuck Niles's head in a toilet bowl?

50 What was the name of the junior high school Frasier and Niles attended?

LEVEL 6
"I'M LISTENING"

1 In what feature film does Kelsey Grammer play a submarine commander? What is the name of his ship?

2 In the Crane household, who likes to drink out of the toilet?

3 Where did David Hyde Pierce go to college?

4 What causes engine problems during Martin's flight to Montana?

5 Which of his costars, according to *Entertainment Weekly*, described Kelsey Grammer as "a big ol' curly bear"?

6 How tall is Kelsey Grammer?

7 What is Roz's last name?

8 What household activity does Niles compare to the Amish custom of barn raising?

9 What insect chases Niles on Frasier's terrace?

10 When Niles was a high school student, what did he carry his gym clothes in? (HINT: It wasn't a gym bag.)

11 Where was Kelsey Grammer born?

12 How much does it cost Niles to remove a pâté stain from his Van Gogh?

13 How did Kelsey Grammer's father die?

14 What *Frasier* cast member was formerly with San Diego's Old Globe Theater?

15 On what soap opera did Kelsey Grammer play a doctor?

16 According to an interview in *People* magazine, what happens to Kelsey Grammer's ankles when he holds in his emotions, thoughts, and feelings?

17 What play did Kelsey Grammer appear in while in high school in 1972?

18 What private school did Kelsey Grammer attend in Fort Lauderdale, Florida?

19 Where did Kelsey Grammer appear in a production of *Measure for Measure*?

20 Whom did Frasier help get elected to the city council in Boston?

21 What power source is required, according to Frasier, to run the TV in the apartment, because Martin watches it so much?

22 What charity benefit with a Hawaiian theme is Niles not invited to?

23 What Native American Indian name does Frasier give Niles?

24 When Martin compares the family to an Oreo cookie, who does he say is the cookie part? Who is the creamy center?

25 What sport do Niles and Frasier play for relaxation and exercise?

26 What is the reason given by the social chairman for the Hoedown for the Homeless for Niles not having received an invitation?

27 Where did Derrick and Gabby Vendercott get their money?

28 Before Martin's hair turned gray, what color was it?

29 TRUE OR FALSE: Eddie has been neutered.

30 What color is the electric guitar Daphne plays on the on-air promotion spots for the show?

31 What household item does Frasier say is a "breeding ground for bacteria"?

32 What does Martin typically spend on a pair of pants for himself?

33 What female movie star and film director calls Frasier's show to complain that her family constantly interrupts her?

34 How does Martin respond when Frasier and Martin invite him to dinner at a restaurant where Niles says "the food is to die for"?

35 Which members of the *Cheers* cast have made guest appearances on *Frasier*?

36 David Angell, Peter Casey, and David Lee are the creators of *Frasier*. What other NBC sitcoms did they produce?

37 In what season of *Cheers* was the character Frasier introduced?

38 Who, in a *USA Today* interview, said of Frasier Crane, "He's got a good heart and is a nice man. When he's out of his element, he always maintains his dignity about him"?

39 What was Kelsey Grammer's favorite *Cheers* episode?

40 Who does Niles say has a "perky little walk"?

41 Of which of his *Frasier* costars has Kelsey Grammer said, "He lives for hot dogs. His life consists of, 'What will I get for it?' It's as though he's been robbed of real love. He lives for the morsels."?

42 What *Frasier* cast member once considered a career as an opera singer?

43 What is Bulldog's last name?

44 Whom does *USA Today* describe as "the finest, fussiest odd couple since Oscar Madison and Felix Unger . . . except this time, they're both Felix"?

45 What character does JoBeth Williams play during her guest spot on *Frasier*?

46 On what tropical island do Lilith and Frasier run into each other when they have adjoining rooms while on vacation?

47 For what film did Mercedes Ruehl win an Oscar?

48 Which of the following celebrities have called into Frasier's radio show?
  A. Terri Hatcher
  B. Terri Garr
  C. Carrie Fisher
  D. Harrison Ford
  E. Tom Hanks

49 Who calls Frasier an "arrogant gasbag"?

50 What city is Jane Leeves from?

LEVEL 7
COUCH POTATOES

1 What is the "Enchanted Grotto"?

2 Who became a bestselling novelist when he wrote a romance novel based on Frasier's real-life affair with a piano teacher?

3 Where did Frasier do his undergraduate work?

4 What did the border guard charge the Cranes with when he stopped their RV on the Canada-Oregon border?

5 Gunar's wife calls into Frasier's talk show when she suspects Gunar of having an extramarital affair. What is her name?

6 What is the name of the handsome stockbroker, with a tan briefcase and cleft chin, Roz wants to date ... until she finds out he is married?

7 What award did *Frasier* win in May of 1995?

8 Kelsey Grammer costarred in the Stephen Sondheim musical *Sunday in the Park With George* with which well-known stage actor? (HINT: He was a regular on the CBS series *Chicago Hope*.)

9 On what piece of furniture, aside from their bed, did Niles and Maris frequently have sex?

10 Which women are paid by Niles to touch him?

11 What wakes Martin up every morning?

12 What consulting position did Frasier hold with the Boston Police Department?

13 What pompous academic did John Mahoney guest-star as on the NBC series *Third Rock From the Sun*?

14 Why can't Sharkbait O'Reilly attend the police department reunion with Martin in Montana?

15 Kelsey Grammer was once a waiter for which restaurant? (HINT: It is part of a chain and specializes in crepes.)

16 When Niles asks Frasier what to do with Aunt Louise's ashes, what is Frasier's glib reply?

17 What does Kate leave at the airport when she moves to Chicago?

18 Where does Frasier eventually want to live?
   A. a mansion
   B. a town house
   C. a penthouse

D. Bermuda

E. a hotel suite

19 When Niles and Frasier tell Martin they can't imagine him and their mother having a sexual relationship, what does Martin jokingly tell them about how he got them?

20 Which of these films does Niles rent for Martin to watch?

A. *The Way We Were*

B. *Funny Girl*

C. *Serpico*

D. *My Dinner with André*

E. *Robocop*

21 What is Kate's favorite color?

22 How many messages does Bob Reynolds leave for Frasier at the radio station within a two-week period?

23 Of whom did Kelsey Grammer once say, "He gave new meaning to the word 'cheap' "?

24 What color is the toilet in Frasier's apartment?

25 When Billy Creasel locked Frasier in a locker in high school, what was Frasier wearing?

26 When Frasier and Niles say they tampered with the "natural order" of things, to what are they referring?

27 What type of plant does Frasier keep on his terrace?

28 Niles was mocked for wearing what clothes to high school?

29 What is plumber Danny Creasel's hourly rate?

30 Who watches neighbors using Frasier's telescope?

31 What difficult piece of classical music does Frasier intend to sing on the public television fund-raiser instead of his usual show tune?

32 What did high school bully Danny Creasel make Niles do with his gym clothes?

33 Who said to *Playboy* magazine, "Frasier is horny, but he is not willing to commit to someone right now"?

34 When Daphne says she "did the deed," to what is she referring?

35 What unusual method does Martin have for drying the kitchen sponge after using it?

36 What unusual method does Martin have for cleaning off the dining room table?

37 What side dish does Martin eat with his breakfast burritos?

38 Who says, "Hoedowns are catnip to postal workers"? What friend of Frasier's is a postal worker?

39 What color underpants does Joe the contractor wear?

40 Why does Frasier keep moving Martin's chair?

41 Which of the Crane brothers has been known to wear a black cowboy hat?

42 Who does Daphne say was wounded in the Falkland Islands war when he was kicked by a sheep which was spooked by an air raid siren?

43 What sarcastic comment does Frasier make when he finds Martin's electric razor in the kitchen?

44 When Martin gains so much weight he has trouble fitting into his pants, what does he wear around the apartment?

45 Who is the parking attendant at the society functions Niles and Maris attend?

46 Who says, "Isn't it sad when bad things happen to good sentences"?

47 Which of the following celebrities have called into Frasier's radio show?
   A. Tom Selleck
   B. Tom Seaver
   C. Tom Hulce
   D. Tom Arnold
   E. Tom Jones

48 What *Frasier* cast member played one of Murphy Brown's secretaries on an episode of *Murphy Brown*?

49 What *Frasier* cast member played Jerry's date on *Seinfeld*?

50 What is Daphne's profession?

LEVEL 8
CRANE OPERATORS

1 Why does Niles take cold showers after he and Maris become separated?

2 What type of dog is Eddie?

3 An arts and entertainment reporter from which daily newspaper described Frasier as "a humbug in search of an accident"?

4 Who describes Frasier's apartment as a "babe magnet"?

5 What type of chair does Martin have?

6 What is the polyester avalanche?

7 What company produces *Frasier* for NBC?

8 What type of dance are Niles and Daphne doing when he tells her he adores her?

9 What canine I.Q. test exercises does Eddie fail?

10 Who says, "It's such a shame when people let fear stop them from trying new things"?

11 Who substitutes for Frasier when he goes on vacation? What is his medical specialty? What is the title of his book?

12 With whom does Maris go on a three-week cruise after separating from Niles?

13 Who is Dora?

14 What does Niles describe as "boring yet difficult"?

15 *Frasier* is a hit NBC show. What are the colors in the NBC logo?

16 What legal professional gives Niles her card and says she'd like him to ask her out on a date?

17 When Martin Crane was separated from Frasier's mother, what city official did he have a crush on?

18 Whom does Niles ask to the Snow Ball?

19 Where is the only place Maris likes to go alone?

20 What color dress does Daphne wear on her "date" with Niles? What does Niles wear? What gift does he give Daphne?

21 Who does Frasier describe as "the scourge of my existence"?

22 What is the name of the receptionist in Niles's office?

23 What is the name of the roman-à-clef play Diane Chambers writes about her life with Frasier and the Cheers gang in Boston? At what Seattle theater is it scheduled to open?

24 What CBS TV series did Diane Chambers write scripts for?

25 What happens to Diane Chambers when she lies?

26 Who comments that Frasier's studio at the radio station looks like the control room at a nuclear missile site?

27 Who says "When you see a man who is well groomed, you know he's not getting any"?

28 Whom does Frasier refer to as a "foul-breathed little Handy Wipe"?

29 Why does Martin sit on a "stakeout" looking through the peephole of the apartment front door?

30 To whom does Diane Chambers refer to as "the queerest little creature"?

31 When was Kelsey Grammer born?

32 What type of shoe is Maris's favorite?

33 What group, according to Niles, "can't get a fair shake in court"?

34 What is it about trucks that gets Niles thinking about sex?

35 Who is the Commodore?

36 What causes a tingling in his chest that Niles at first thinks is produced by a testosterone rush?

37 What hoodlum does Niles ask to "fix" Maris's parking tickets and moving violations?

38 When Niles tells Frasier, "She rejected you in the most debilitating way a man can be rejected," to whom is he referring?

39 What does Frasier tell his listeners is "the key to lasting weight loss"?

40 Like what kind of nut does Frasier say Niles will crack under pressure?

41 What is the highest-calorie, highest-cholesterol drink Frasier ever ordered at the coffee bar?

42 When Niles asks Frasier if he still loves Diane Chambers, and Frasier says no, what does Niles accuse him of?

43 Who refers to the advice Frasier gives over the air as "half-assed"?

44 What type of food does Frasier especially enjoy at a luau?

45 What two words had Maris never said to Niles until after they were separated?

46 When Diane broke his heart by leaving him at the altar, what, according to Frasier, did she leave in its place?

47 Why do Daphne's psychic powers falsely lead her to believe that the small-time hoodlum Niles is dealing with to help Maris is an osteopath?

48 Who says, "A little mistrust adds mystery to a relationship"?

49 What cross-dressing caller asks Frasier for advice on losing weight so he can fit into women's clothing better?

50 Where did Diane Chambers live after leaving Boston and achieving success as a writer?

LEVEL 9
GOOD NIGHT, SEATTLE!

1 Live specimens of which creature are kept in a fish tank in the kitchen of the restaurant Niles and Frasier buy?

2 Who was Frasier's piano teacher when he was in high school?

3 Why does Niles's maid, Marta, speak fluent German?

4 At what hotel do Niles, Frasier, and Martin Crane stay during their ice-fishing trip?

5 Who is Harlo Safford's lawyer?

6 According to Niles, how long should the foreplay and cuddling portions of sex take?

7 What temperature does the thermometer reach in February in Seattle when Frasier speculates global warming is causing the climate to heat up?

8 With what food does Martin's friend Jimmy celebrate his birthday each year?

9 Who says, "It is unwise to slide down a fire pole wearing wool pants"?

10 Who is the restaurant critic on Frasier's radio station?

11 What stunt did Frasier's agent pull during contract negotiations with the radio station?

12 What ex-boss of Frasier's at the radio station thought Frasier was gay and was romantically interested in him?

13 For what famous director did Kelsey Grammer perform during his audition for Julliard?

14 Which *Frasier* cast member starred in the made-for-TV movie *The Innocent*?

15 Who says of Daphne, "If you had ever smelled her hair, you'd know she is worth one more try. She is an angel, a goddess"?

16 What TV character does Kelsey Grammer provide the voice for on *The Simpsons*? What children's performer does this character work for until he is sent to prison?

17 Who said, "We all loved Aunt Louise ... even if the camera didn't"?

18 On what piece of furniture does Niles sit when he relaxes at home?

19 What job does handyman Joe DeCarlo do for Maris's neighbor and friend Mimsi Stanhope?

    A. wax her runners

    B. buff her cabinets

    C. strip her entryway

    D. polish her knockers

    E. fix her heater

20 Who tells Niles, "Only the truth shall make you clot"?

21 What is Frasier's favorite musical?

22 Who has a twin sister living in Chicago?

23 What is Bob Reynolds's nickname?

24 Of what *Frasier* actor did *People* magazine say, "Our dear friend obviously suffered from a deep-rooted fear of abandonment and a strong desire to be needed, twin pathologies that led to a pattern of self-destructive behavior and notable appearances in the *National Enquirer*"?

25 What regular from the TV series *The Five Mrs. Buchanans* plays Bebe Glaser?

26 Of whom does *Entertainment Weekly* say he has turned his *Frasier* role into "a complicated, endlessly fascinating character"?

27 Where did Kelsey Grammer meet his girlfriend, Tammi Alexander?

28 What is Niles's psychiatric diagnosis of why Danny Creasel was a bully in high school? Why does Danny say he did it?

29 Who tells Niles, "A civilized person can do anything in a calm, rational manner," then sticks someone's head in the toilet?

30 What *Frasier* cast member is quoted in *Playboy* as saying, "I think anybody who's brilliantly talented is open to being misunderstood"?

31 Which of the following songs does Kelsey Grammer like to play on the piano?
    A. "Feelings"
    B. "New York, New York"
    C. "Summertime"
    D. the *Cheers* theme
    E. the *Frasier* theme

32 What were Kelsey Grammer's nicknames when he was growing up?

33 What porno movie was Kelsey Grammer asked to star in for a fee of ten thousand dollars?

34 During his performance in what stage play was Kelsey Grammer interrupted by an earthquake registering 6.1 on the Richter scale?

35 What theme park did Kelsey Grammer design when he was eight years old?

36 How does Frasier describe the viewership of Seattle's public television station?

37 What *Frasier* cast member told *Cosmopolitan* magazine, "American audiences want to be played up to. They want sophisticated comedy that makes them think. When they think, they laugh more"?

38 Which of the following celebrities has made a call to Frasier's radio show?
   A. Marlon Brando
   B. Matthew Broderick
   C. Jonathan Taylor Thomas
   D. Jeremy Irons
   E. Nathan Lane

39 What *Frasier* cast member once stuffed packages at a fingernail accessory company?

40 What historical village does Frasier take Frederick to for their vacation?

41 On the canine I.Q. test, which of these breeds does Eddie score higher than?
   A. collie
   B. poodle
   C. beagle
   D. German shepherd

E. Labrador

F. none of the above

42 What are the names of Jane Leeves's cats?

43 Who is Niles's "mole" in Maris's house?

44 What is the first dance Daphne teaches Niles when she gives him dance lessons?

45 Which of these activities does Martin say Niles was good at as a child?

A. riding his bicycle

B. jumping rope

C. kicking a ball

D. none of the above

46 What does Niles ask Frasier to do in exchange for Niles making a large pledge to the public TV station in Seattle?

47 Niles says what type of man is "all over Maris" like "ants on a Snickers bar"?

48 According to an article Martin read, how long does it take the average border collie to remove a towel placed over its head?

49 What Latin band leader, formerly married to Charo, is one of Daphne's favorite musicians?

50 During what dance does Daphne tell Niles their bodies must be in "continuous contact" with "not a sliver of daylight between us"?

LEVEL 10
FRASIER HAS LEFT
THE BUILDING

1 Whose presence in Seattle, according to Niles, causes dogs to form into packs and blood to weep from walls?

2 What patient is Niles seeing when Frasier bursts into his office and interrupts the session?

3 Who says, "We're still human . . . we have to do what feels good sometimes, don't we?"

4 Why is Diane Chambers fired from the CBS TV series for which she writes?

5 When Diane invites Frasier to be the first to see her play in rehearsal, what does Martin think she's asking him for?

6 How far is the walk from Frasier's apartment to the coffee shop where he and Niles hang out?

7 When Martin says, "I wonder if this is the pride old man Kennedy felt when his boys played touch football together," to what is he referring?

8 What strange behavior does Maris exhibit when she and Niles go out to dinner with Diane and Frasier?

9 Frasier jokingly says Martin could have been the security coordinator for what late union leader?

10 What happens to Maris when she sees expensive shoes she wants to buy?

11 Who says, "I think the law should treat everyone the same"?

12 Why does Frasier think Maris cannot be imprisoned in an ordinary jail cell?

13 What brand of overcoat does Joseph Belasco wear?

14 What reason does Frasier give Martin for financially backing Diane Chambers's new play?

15 As a child, what did Maris steal from the Vatican?

16 Who does Roz refer to as the "little weasel"?

17 Which boyfriend of Roz's has been in trouble with the police?

18 In Diane's play about Cheers, what name does she give to the character representing Frasier?

19 What sucks Niles "into a vortex of rage and despair"?

20 Of whom does Frasier say, "She's ounces of fun"?

21 What subcontractor provided the cement used in the construction of Frasier's apartment building?

22 Martin says he would rather see Frasier stuffed into what object than have him get back together with Diane Chambers?

23 For how long have Jerome Belasco and Brandy been "semi-engaged" when Jerome approaches Frasier for counseling?

24 Who frequently orders double espresso at the coffee bar?

25 When Jerome Belasco is displeased, what happens to him? What does he take to remedy this condition?

26 How many jobs has Brandy been fired from? What position does Niles hire her for?

27 When Eddie is injured in a dog fight and must wear a cone to prevent him from scratching or biting his wounds, why do Martin and Daphne have him sit on top of the TV set?

28 Who says, "Too often we shrink from doing things we really want to do"?

29 What has a woman done when she has "dipped her toe into Crane Lake"?

30 How much did the kite Niles flew at Wilson's Meadow when he was a child cost?

31 For how long had Martin been secretly writing songs he wanted Frank Sinatra to sing?

32 What business is located in the office below Niles's psychiatry practice?

33 Who says, "Sometimes in life you must do unpleasant things"?

34 Who wrote the *Frasier* episode featuring the sword fight between Niles and Gunthar?

35 What Crane family member is hypoglycemic?

36 How much does ad revenue during Frasier's time slot increase during his first year of broadcasting his radio show?

37 Who was Kelsey Grammer's first wife?

38 Who makes love faster than the time it takes to get a vaccination?

39 Who says, "Everything doesn't have to be perfect"?

40 How many times has Frasier gone jogging in his life?

41 On what vehicles does the radio station run ads for Frasier's show?

42 What wine does Niles promise to bring to dinner when Diane Chambers visits?

43 What time does Niles pick up Daphne for their date?

44 Which of the following did Martin do routinely while a police officer?
   A. fix parking tickets
   B. eat for free at the local diner
   C. get free coffee and donuts from the donut shop
   D. accept small bribes
   E. none of the above

45 Whom does Frasier refer to as "Bugsy"?

46 What hoodlum's mother nags him because he's not married?

47 Who tells Frasier, "Your feelings are stupid"?

48 Who does Frasier say lives in "a tortured little world"?

49 When Frasier fleetingly fantasizes about killing his father, how does he imagine he would do it?

50 Which rock-and-roll star lives in the penthouse directly above Frasier's apartment?

BONUS QUESTION

What is the jet pack?

ANSWER KEY

Level 1
Tossed Salad

1 "What growing boy doesn't?"

2 Princeton High School, Class of 1976

3 Right

4 A clipper-class schooner

5 Armani

6 Mont Blanc

7 Five percent

8 Christopher Lloyd

9 A burst appendix

10 Kate Costas, his boss

11 Noel Shenski

12 A BMW

13 Frasier to Kate Costas

14 1, C; 2, A; 3, E; 4, B; 5, D; 6, F; 7, H; 8, G

15 Mrs. Kelly

16 Crane and Crane Psychiatry

17 Half a million

18 Ninth

19 Her wine club

20 "Hello, this is Dr. Frasier Crane. . . . I'm listening."

21 Seattle

22 A Mercedes Benz

23 Works as a ballroom dancer

24 Braised carrots; creamed onions

25 Deirdre Sauvage

26 Kate Costas

27 A Steinway baby grand; $47,000

28 "Happy Chef"

29 Kate Costas

30 A black BMW

31 He writes songs for Frank Sinatra.

32 KACL; 780 AM

33 Great-Aunt Louise Crane

34 Wilson's Meadow; getting his kite out of a tree

35 A Colt 45 APC with a single-stack magazine

36 Father Mike

37 Music

38 Kelsey Grammer

39 Bull & Finch

40 Spring of 1993

41 John Mahoney appeared in one episode during the last season of *Cheers*.

42 Sparky

43 Julie Faraday

44 Daphne

45 B

46 B

47 Bebe Glaser

48 *Caroline in the City*

49 Miles O'Shea

50 Norm Peterson

Level 2
Scrambled Eggs

1 She went to live in an experimental underground biosphere.

2 Nanny Gee, a children's entertainer

3 *Court TV*

4 Beth

5 Rocky

6 Great-Aunt Meryl

7 E

8 11:55 P.M.

9 A star sapphire pinkie ring

10 A four-breasted female character Noel Shemski wants to see on *Star Trek*

11 A goldfish pond

12 Daphne Moon

13 She goes on a "sake's alive, I'm thirty-five" shopping spree.

14 Glen and Les Charles

15 He breaks out in hives.

16 He tried to double-bill her for fireplace andirons.

17 Nanette

18 They are characters on a soap opera Martin and Daphne watch.

19 "Hands of Hercules"

20 Matthew Pym

21 Double latte with chocolate shavings

22 A sack of flour

23 *Wings*

24 Unloaded fishing boats

25 His nose bleeds

26 B

27 The *Virgin Island Review*

28 A, B, C, D, E, F, G

29 Luke Tarsitano

30 Clinical psychosis

31 Roy Christopher, the show's production designer

32 Paramount Studios, Stage 25

33 $981,182.12

34 Cafe Nervosa

35 Forty-eight thousand dollars a year

36 *Christmas in Washington*

37 B, D

38 He thinks he can score with her.

39 Maris has canceled it.

40 Candy Cane

41 "Almost any sophisticated remark"

42 Cognitive skills and deductive reasoning

43 He thinks he is being maced.

44 He is the little goat herder in a Christmas parable Frasier reads on the air.

45 The Bernsteins

46 Franklin Crane

47 A Rudolph the Red-Nosed Reindeer wreath

48 Looking for rat hairs in hot dogs

49 He tells him Maris is in a coma.

50 An Outlaw Laser Robo-Geek

Level 3
A Bit Confused

1 Otto

2 Mirage

3 Seventeen

4 The change in food caused the dog to flatulate frequently.

5 Captain of the starship U.S.S. *Bozeman*

6 A, B, C

7 B, C, E, F, G

8 *The Mask*

9 A sensory deprivation tank

10 Dr. Schachtner; Aruba

11 B, C, D

12 They make love.

13 Tossed salad and scrambled eggs

14 Pinks and yellows

15 African art

16 Rossino's

17 He has sex with Kate in the broadcast booth and it is heard over the air.

18 Deirdre Sauvage

19 Lemon cake

20 Wisconsin

21 B

22 "Fast-food psychiatry"—what Niles terms Frasier's approach to therapy

23 D

24 A starter's pistol

25 Bartok's Concerto in C

26 Six Golden Mike awards and one Peabody

27 A Doberman

28 O'Neal's

29 Kelsey Grammer

30 Harriet Sansom Harris

31 D

32 Lilith

33 Sam Malone

34 Aerobics

35 She hosts a radio show on gardening.

36 She feeds her one of Eddie's dog biscuits.

37 Watch a family member be autopsied

38 Bebe Glasier

39 Eight percent

40 Daphne

41 Cracked gas pipes

42 D

43 990 WPT

44 "She's Such a Groovy Lady"

45 Throw him in front of a bus

46 Alberta Leonard

47 Good mental health

48 A wine club

49 Joe DeCarlo

50 D

Level 4
The Blues A-Callin'

1 Cecil

2 Lift things

3 Senator Adler

4 Xenophobia

5 Four times an hour

6 45 degrees

7 A friend of Martin's whom Martin occasionally corresponds with

8 C

9 Convert the station to an all-talk format

10 Daphne

11 Niles

12 Tony

13 Daphne

14 She works as an art director

15 Arctic silver

16 Louie

17 True

18 Three

19 Kate Costas

20 *All Dogs Go to Heaven: II*

21 A lizard

22 They both are diminutive people wearing scanty silk clothes and carrying riding crops.

23 The members of his wine club

24 They burned down the garage by accident.

25 Roz

26 Frasier

27 A french fry vending machine his caller George wants him to invest five thousand dollars in

28 Tacoma; dead squirrels

29 Comb his hair

30 Mark Twain first editions

31 Niles's dermatologist

32 Mesquite soaked in water for ten minutes; Cheyenne smoked quail

33 He is a children's photographer at Value Mart.

34 Prunes, carob, and miscellaneous fruits mixed in a blender

35 "I love you and I want to have your baby."

36 In both professions, "you skim the surface, explore the murky depths, and add chemicals when necessary."

37 Jack Benny

38 Niles

39 $150 an hour

40 Mercedes E3-20

41 Stick their head in the toilet bowl and flush

42 Danny Creasel

43 Kelsey Grammer

44 Maris

45 Seventy-eight years old; Irene Olga

46 Champ

47 Frasier is Freudian and Niles is Jungian.

48 A research scientist

49 *The Powers That Be*

50 Kelsey Grammer

Level 5
The Id and the Ego

1 Maurice; Emilio's

2 Ken Griffey Jr.

3 A single red rose

4 *Wolf*

5 *Moonstruck*

6 Cheers

7 Duke's

8 Clarinet lessons

9 Harvard

10 Four hours

11 Bavaria

12 Strudel Boy

13 James Burrows

14 Best Comedy on Television

15 "Buy me a Mercedes and I'll make your neck look like a relief map of the Andes."

16 Eight

17 She is allergic to roses.

18 Kelsey Grammer

19 Judge Richard McCarron

20 His positive attitude

21 His pants fall down.

22 Seventy-eight and a half years old

23 When it becomes soft while he's taking a bath, he peels it off.

24 Nonfat milk

25 "Buttons and Bows"

26 Maris asked him to go to the drugstore.

27 Jaclyn Smith

28 Aunt Louise

29 Color it over with a yellow magic marker

30 Satisfy Maris

31 Bad wiring

32 The glockenspiel

33 He is allergic to cats.

34 Kate Costas

35 Paris

36 C

37 Kate Costas

38 To mark the one Niles dropped on the floor

39 Zero

40 Beer

41 Bob Reynolds

42 Frasier's suggestion that the show get an unlisted number

43 Forest fires

44 Ralph

45 Hats

46 Agoura, California

47 Mercedes Benz S Class

48 Frasier's attempt to fix the toilet

49 "There goes Crane, down the drain."

50 John Adams Junior High

Level 6
"I'm Listening"

1 *Down Periscope*; U.S.S. *Stingray*

2 Eddie

3 Yale

4 Canadian geese fly into the engine, resulting in mechanical failure that forces the plane to turn back.

5 Jane Leeves

6 Six feet two inches

7 Doyle

8 Fixing the toilet

9 In Niles's words, "A bee the size of a wood finch"

10 A valise

11 St. Thomas in the Virgin Islands

12 $4,000

13 He was shot in the head, at home, by a mentally ill intruder.

14 Kelsey Grammer

15 *Another World*

16 They swell up.

17 *The Little Foxes*

18 Pine Crest

19 Mark Taper Forum in Los Angeles

20 Woody Boyd

21 A nuclear power plant

22 The Luau for Lupus

23 Waltzes With Snobs

24 Martin and Frasier are the cookie part; Daphne is the creamy center

25 Squash

26 He says his dog ate it.

27 They inherited family money made in timber.

28 Brown

29 True

30 Yellow

31 A wet sponge in the kitchen sink

32 Fifteen dollars

33 Jodie Foster

34 "Your country is to die for; food is to eat."

35 Shelley Long, Bebe Neuwirth, Ted Danson

36 *Wings* and *Cheers*

37 The second season

38 Kelsey Grammer

39 "Dinner at Eightish"

40 Roz

41 Moose

42 Kelsey Grammer

43 Briscoe

44 Frasier and Niles

45 Madeline, Frasier's girlfriend

46 Bora Bora

47 *The Fisher King*

48 B, C

49 Kate Costas

50 Manchester, England

Level 7
Couch Potatoes

1 The table for two near the kitchen door in the Cranes's restaurant

2 Thomas J. Fellow

3 Harvard

4 Transporting fruit over the border

5 Gretchen

6 Gary

7 The Peabody Award

8 Mandy Patinkin

9 A sixteenth-century gilt wood couch

10 His manicurist, pedicurist, and facialist

11 Eddie licking his face

12 He was their suicide prevention psychologist.

13 Dr. Leonard Hanlin

14 He's dead.

15 The Magic Pan

16 "Winter's coming. The sidewalks will be icy."

17 Her cat

18 C

19 He found them at a church picnic in wicker baskets floating down the river

20 A

21 Blue

22 Forty-five

23 Jack Benny

24 Black

25 A girl's field hockey uniform

26 Their attempt to do manual labor

27 A ficus tree

28 A tweed blazer with elbow patches

29 Fifty-nine dollars an hour

30 Daphne and Martin

31 An aria from Verdi's *Rigoletto*

32 He put his jock strap over his head and made him wear it like a tiara.

33 Kelsey Grammer

34 She had sex.

35 He puts it in the toaster.

36 He has Eddie lick it off.

37 Tater Tots

38 Niles; Cliff Clavin

39 Blue

40 It interferes with the synergy of the room's flow.

41 Niles

42 Joe the contractor

43 "All our appliances are on an adventure this weekend!"

44 Underwear and sweatpants

45 Nelson

46 Kate Costas

47 C

48 Jane Leeves

49 Jane Leeves

50 Physical therapist

Level 8
Crane Operators

1 The coldness reminds him of Maris.

2 A Jack Russell terrier

3 The *Los Angeles Times*

4 Sam Malone

5 A La-Z-Boy

6 A fat lady who slides onto Martin during an emergency airplane exit

7 Grub Street Productions

8 The tango

9 Finding a specific toy (usually a toy banana) and removing a towel from his head

10 Daphne

11 Gareth Woton; podiatry; *Bunions and Blisters and Corns, Oh My!*

12 Pearson Broadwater

13 She is Niles's childhood pen pal from Costa Rica.

14 Dancing

15 From left to right: yellow, orange, red, purple, blue, green

16 Claire Barnes

17 A coroner at the city morgue

18 Margerie Nash

19 Bed

20 Red; a tuxedo; a red rose

21 Diane Chambers

22 Lucille

23 *Rhapsody and Requiem*; The Roundabout

24 *Dr. Quinn, Medicine Woman*

25 She gets a tic in her cheek.

26 Martin

27 Niles

28 Eddie

29 Someone is stealing their newspaper.

30 Maris

31 February 20, 1952

32 Ferragamo pumps

33 Wealthy white women

34 Sexy drawings on the truck mud flaps

35 Maris's father

36 The vibration of his cellular phone

37 Jerome Belasco

38 Diane Chambers

39 "Change the way you view food every day."

40 A Jordan almond

41 Latte mocha with whipped cream and a strip of bacon

42 Being in classic denial

43 Martin Crane

44 Poi ramekins

45 "Thank you"

46 A "sucking chest wound"

47 She sees him hovering over people with broken bones.

48 Frasier

49 Steve

50 A beach house in Malibu

Level 9
Good Night, Seattle!

1 Eels

2 Clarise Warner

3 She worked for a German family after the war.

4 The Bed and Bass Hotel

5 Mr. Jurow

6 Thirty minutes

7 80 degrees Fahrenheit

8 "The big ham"

9 Frasier

10 Gil Chesterfield

11 She fakes a suicide attempt by standing on a window ledge.

12 Tom Durant

13 John Houseman

14 Kelsey Grammer

15 Niles

16 Sideshow Bob; Crusty the Clown

17 Martin Crane

18 His oxblood leather wing-back easy chair

19 C

20 Frasier

21 *Candide*

22 Kate Costas

23 Shishka-Bob

24 Kelsey Grammer

25 Harriet Harris

26 David Hyde Pierce

27 Harry O's, a restaurant in Manhattan Beach, California

28 Acts of misplaced aggression aimed at his father; Danny said picking on people was the only thing he was good at, and he wanted to please his father.

28 Frasier

30 Kelsey Grammer

31 C

32 Elsie the Cow, Graham Cracker

33 *The Bermuda Triangle*

34 *Richard II*

35 Grammerland

36 "Discerning, cultured"

37 Kelsey Grammer

38 B

39 Jane Leeves

40 Colonial Williamsburg

41 F

42 Matilda and Newman (after the *Seinfeld* character)

43 Marta

44 The fox trot

45 D

46 Stop singing

47 Gigolos

48 Seven seconds

49 Xavier Cugat

50 The tango

Level 10
Frasier Has Left the Building

1 Lilith

2 Mr. Carr

3 Frasier

4 She accidentally sets Jane Seymour's hair on fire with a branding iron while atte..npting to show the actress the proper way to cauterize a wound on the set of her show.

5 Sex

6 Thirty-two blocks

7 Frasier and Niles powdering pastry together in Frasier's kitchen

8 She gets sick eating everyone's sorbet and asks the coat girl to massage her abdomen.

9 Jimmy Hoffa

10 She loses her hand-eye coordination and has a car accident.

11 Martin

12 She is so skinny she can slip through the space between the bars.

13 Armani

14 Because it is tax deductible

15 A crucifix

16 Niles

17 Phil

18 Franklin

19 His separation from Maris

20 Maris

21 Jerome Belasco's brother

22 The body of a dead horse

23 Eight years

24 Niles

25 Acid in his stomach; hot milk

26 Fourteen; receptionist in his office

27 It improves TV reception—especially channel 5

28 Frasier

29 She has had sex with one of the Crane brothers.

30 Thirty-nine cents

31 Thirty years

32 A medical testing laboratory

33 Jerome Belasco

34 Chuck Ranberg and Anne Flett-Giordano

35 Maris

36 11.5 percent

37 Doreen Alderman

38 Jerome Belasco

39 Martin Crane

40 Once

41 Buses

42 A "cheeky bordeaux"

43 Seven P.M.

44 E

45 Niles

46 Jerome Belasco's

47 Martin

48 Niles

49 By stuffing a kitchen sponge in his mouth

50 Freddie Chainsaw

BONUS QUESTION

Putting a fire extinguisher down someone's pants and turning it on

ABOUT THE AUTHOR

Bob Bly is the author of more than thirty books, including *The Ultimate Unauthorized Star Trek Quiz Book* (Harper-Collins) and *Comic Book Heroes: 1,101 Trivia Questions About America's Favorite Superheroes.* (Carol Publishing Group). He watches too much TV for his own good.

Questions and comments on *What's Your Frasier I.Q.?* may be sent to:

Bob Bly
22 East Quackenbush Avenue
Dumont, NJ 07628

E-mail: Rwbly@aol.com